# PAKI WAITARA

MYTHS & LEGENDS
*of the*
MĀORI

# PAKI WAITARA

## MYTHS & LEGENDS
### *of the*
# MĀORI

### QUEENIE RIKIHANA HYLAND

REED

Published by Reed Books, a division of Reed Publishing (NZ) Ltd, 39 Rawene Road, Birkenhead, Auckland 10. Associated companies, branches and representatives throughout the world.

ISBN 0 7900 0553 0

Cover design and illustration by Clair Stutton
Printed in New Zealand

# He mihi

During the writing of this book my beloved mother Ra Awatea Rikihana passed away; then shortly before *Paki Waitara* was completed her first great grandchild Hoani Colwell Taylor was born. It is fitting then that I dedicate this book to both the old and new generations.

# Contents

# Acknowledgements

There are many people to thank for the help they have given in compiling this book. Advice and support has come from my own whanaunga, most particularly Auntie Theresa (who gave the book its name) and Uncle Paddy Rikihana, Auntie Queenie Johnson, Miki Rikihana and Auntie Gabrielle Rikihana.

I acknowledge, too, the family of Pei Te Hurinui Jones who allowed me to use the Tūrongo and Māhinārangi love story, which in many ways is the jewel in the crown of these Paki Waitara. As that legend also tells the history of my own tipuna, from whom all Ngāti Raukawa are descended, then it is also entirely appropriate that it is included.

Others talked to during the writing of the book have been Professor Whatarangi Winiata, Te Ahukaramu Charles Royal, Sir Tipene O'Regan and Te Waari Carkeek.

# Introduction

If I have discovered anything while compiling this collection of stories for *Paki Waitara*, it is that many writers have gone before me telling the myths and legends of Māori *as they have seen them*. In fact, that is traditionally what 'paki waitara' meant — having different storytellers each tell their own versions of the legends and the listeners then decide for themselves the stories' meanings or conclusions.

This, too, was my aim: to read and listen to as many legends as I could, and then to write my own versions. In this way my research has been diverse, and to some extent the bibliography I have supplied does not include all of the sources I have used. But paramount for me was to give the new reader a taste of the stories that have been written about since the likes of Sir George Grey first employed Māori translators to record oral tribal histories last century. If anything has become clear it is that there are many, many more stories yet to be unearthed and brought to light.

My hope is that these *Paki Waitara* will bring together in one book everyone's favourite legends, plus a couple of new surprises.

*Queenie Rikihana Hyland*

# The Creation

# The Creation

In the beginning, before there was light, the world as we
know it was darkness and nothing — Te Kore, the
Nothingness.

Te Pō-nui — The Great Night
Te Pō-roa — The Long Night
Te Pō-uriuri — The Dark Night
Te Pō-kerekere — The Intensely Dark Night
Te Pō-tiwha — The Gloom-laden Night
Te Pō-tangotango — The Night to be Felt
Te Pō-tē-kitea — The Night Unseen

Out of the stillness and dimness the beginnings of life
stirred from the nothing.

Rangi-nui, the Sky Father, looked down with loving eyes
into the beauty of Papa-tū-ā-nuku, the Earth Mother. He

had longed for her from above and slowly they moved towards each other until they came together and were joined in a close, loving embrace.

The offspring of Rangi and Papa were numerous, and they lived in the cramped darkness between their parents. The Sky lay on the Earth and no light could come between them. Her coverings were rank low weed, and the sea was dark and putrid.

At length the children of Rangi and Papa came together to decide what should be done about their parents so that they could stand, stretch and grow. 'Shall we kill our parents or shall we separate them?' they asked.

Tū-mata-uenga, the fiercest son and the god of war, said simply: 'We have no choice. Let us kill our mother and father!'

But Tāne-mahuta, father of all the forests, protested and said, 'No, no, it is better that they be prised apart. Let our father stand high above us and our mother remain close to us below and continue to be our nursing mother.'

All of the sons agreed it should be done except for Tāwhiri-matea, the god of winds and storms. He vowed to wage war forever on anyone who ripped his parents apart.

First Rongo-mā-tāne, god of cultivated food, tried to force the Heavens from the Earth. But he failed and next Tangaroa, god of all things that live in the sea, rose up. He tried valiantly but he too failed. Next Haumia Tiketike, god of uncultivated food, tried, also without success.

Tū-mata-uenga, god of war, leapt into the task, hacking wildly at the sinews that bound Earth and Sky, making them bleed. It is with this act that the sacred red clay, or ochre, was made. But even Tū, the fiercest of the sons, could not sever Rangi from his lover Papa.

Now there was only Tāne-mahuta left. He took a more measured approach. Over an immense length of time he grew as the kauri tree, and very slowly he tried to move his parents. Next he lay on his back on his Earth Mother and he placed his feet against his father the Sky, and eventually the Sky began to move. Cries and shrieks of pain rang out from Rangi and Papa. 'Why, why are you doing this to our great love for each other?' they cried.

The sinews that bound them stretched and ripped asunder, and with one final thrust Rangi was hurled far away, high above his beloved Papa.

Now Tāwhiri-matea, who had been holding his breath in anger, rose up and rushed about clearing away the rank air that still clung to his mother. It was he alone who would choose to follow his father into the realms above. But before joining his father, Tāwhiri waged war against his brothers — knocking down the massive tree trunks of Tāne and churning up and lashing at the shores of Tangaroa. Luckily, Papa the Earth Mother came to the rescue of her peaceful sons, Rongo (the fern root) and Haumia (the kūmara), snatching them away and hiding them deep within her where Tāwhiri could not find them.

Tū, the god of war, was the only son brave enough to withstand the lightning and storms of his brother. He stood his ground against Tāwhiri, firmly placing his feet on the breast of his mother as his brother howled and raged about him.

When at last Tāwhiri had calmed down, his rage spent, he left to join his father in the heavens. Peace descended into the space between the Earth and the Sky. Now the multitudes of creatures whom Rangi and Papa had begotten came to life and crawled about on the land.

But Rangi, the Sky, looked down upon his wife and in his longing shed vast quantities of tears so that much of the land was covered by the sea. Papa, the Earth, looked up at her husband and in her yearning she too wept for him.

At length one of Papa's many sons, Mataaho, became worried that all of the land would be covered with sea from his father's tears so he resolved to turn his mother over so that his parents could not forever look upon one another and continue their grieving. This he accomplished, and now when Rangi weeps his tears are the dewdrops on Papa's back; the early morning mists that gather in her valleys are her heartfelt sighs.

When Papa was turned over her son Rūaumoko was still at her breast, and to keep warm he became the god of earthquakes and volcanic fire. When he walks about his rumblings can be felt above as earthquakes.

Tāne-mahuta looked about him and felt sorry for his mother Papa in her nakedness. He raced about the land clothing her body in all the beauty of living things not dreamt of in the dark world. Trees, birds, bees and living things of every hue and colour he brought to life. He urged the creatures to sing and flit about the forest to bring cheer to his mother in her unhappiness.

Looking up, he sought also to clothe the darkness of his father, Rangi, who sprawled cold and grey in the vastness above. He took the bright sun and put it on Rangi's back, and the shining moon and put it in the front. He travelled through the heavens and found a garment glowing red. This he spread from east to west and north to south. But once in place he decided it was too much and in his haste to rip it off a small fragment remained in the west. This can still be seen today at the time of the setting sun.

But still he was not happy — the nights were long and dark before Marama the Moon brightened the night sky.

Tāne-mahuta journeyed far to the ends of the world, to Maunganui, the Great Mountain, where the Shining Ones lived. There he found his brother Uru and begged him to give up some of his children so that the Shining Ones could be fastened onto the mantle of the Sky. Uru gave a great shout and the little Shining Ones came rolling and frolicking up the hill to their father. Tāne-mahuta gathered the glowing mass of lights into a great basket and this he spilled into a dark blue mantle, forming the Milky Way.

Next he journeyed to Mahiku-rangi, to the House of the Guardian of the Stars, Tupu-renga-o-te-Pō — The Growing Night. There he sought and was given the morning stars — Toko-meha, Lonely South, and Te-Paetai-o-te-Rangi, Shore of Heaven.

The four sacred holders of the world — Hira-utu, Fish by the Land; Hira-tai, Fish of the Sea; Pari-nuku, Fish by the Sea; and Pari-rangi, Cliff of the Heavens — he placed at the four corners of the compass.

Lastly he took the five stars — Ao-tahi, Puaka, Tuku-rua, Tama-rereti and Te-Waka-a-Tama-rereti — and he formed a cross in the south.

When finally his work was finished Tāne-mahuta looked up in awe at Rangi, his father, and declared that truly his beauty was indescribable; he was an ariki, like his beautiful forest- and fern-clad wife Papa-tū-ā-nuku beneath him.

# Māui,
# the Demi-god

# Māui,
# the Demi-god

Māui personified everything the Māori could want from a demi-god. The myths that surround him bring to life the cheeky mischief-maker who went on to become feared, worshipped and admired. After a miraculous birth and upbringing he set out to find his parents and to win their affection. He caused mayhem when he played with fire, but he also brought new arts, he discovered a new land by pulling it up out of the sea, and he tamed te rā, the sun.

## Māui's birth

Māui's inauspicious birth was an important factor in how the demi-god of mischief came to cause trouble for the human race, always hurting them out of spite.

He came to be called Māui-tikitiki-a-Taranga, as it was in the tikitiki or topknot of his mother Taranga that he was wrapped and thrown out to sea. He was her fifth son — the child of her old age — and she thought the baby had died in her womb, so she wrapped him in her hair and tossed him into the sea.

Māui should have been buried with special ceremonies, as was the custom of the time. If this was not done he could become an evil spirit, hell-bent on causing mischief and trouble. But Māui did not die and his discovery and subsequent upbringing with Tama-nui-ki-te-Rangi meant Māui-pōtiki (the infant) was to learn many great things. Tama rescued him from the seashore, where he found the baby still wrapped in his mother's hair and nestled in sea kelp, which had kept Māui afloat and alive.

As Māui-pōtiki grew up he learned many tricks, he learned powerful incantations, and he learned how to take on the shape of birds. Eventually the time came for Māui to take leave of the old man Tama, who had been both mother and father to him. He set off to journey to the place where he would find his own people. After many days of walking through forests, around lakes and over mountains he came to the village where he knew his people lived. He walked into the wharenui where the people were gathered.

Māui saw a beautiful woman talking to her four sons. 'Come, my sons,' she was telling them, 'you must get ready for when the singing and dancing begins. Māui-mua (Māui the first), stand here; now Māui-roto (Māui the middle), next to him. Māui-taha (Māui the side), that's three sons, and finally Māui-pae (Māui the edge) is the fourth and the last.'

But just then Māui stepped out of the shadows and said: 'I'm your son Māui too.'

Taranga was amazed and not a little annoyed at the intrusion of the handsome young boy. She questioned him, asking did he come from the east, west, south or the north. To all these questions he answered 'No.'

Then she asked, 'Did you come on the waves of the sea?' and Māui said 'Yes.'

Finally she asked, 'Did you come on the waves of the wind?'

'Yes,' young Māui answered.

Then Taranga cried out: 'It is true. It is true. He is the son to whom I gave birth but I cast him into the sea because his time was not ripe. He lived! He is alive! He is my son! He shall be called Māui-tikitiki-a-Taranga.'

In the festivities that followed Māui performed some of the many tricks he had learnt. The people were astounded when the young boy uttered the incantations that could turn him into a brightly coloured kererū, or pigeon.

Everyone was delighted with Māui except his four brothers. They were jealous of the young upstart who had come into their lives and had taken the affection of their beloved mother, Taranga.

These feelings would be compounded when Taranga called to her young son to join her on her sleeping mat. The brothers could only watch as Taranga rolled out her mat, drew a cloak over herself and Māui, and draped a protective arm over her new-found son.

## Māui meets his father, Makea-tū-tara

Māui grew up tall and strong like his brothers, but two things made him stand out as different — he had an ill-formed, flattened head, and the red eyes of a fearless warrior. As he grew up he was forever getting into trouble for playing nasty tricks on others, or for using magic that caused confusion and admiration in equal doses.

Māui was satisfied that he had found his mother but he also wanted to meet his father, Makea-tū-tara. Each day Taranga would rise at dawn and go into the Underworld to visit her husband, then as night fell she would return to her sons.

Māui decided to turn himself into a pigeon and follow his mother. When Māui appeared before his father, Makea was astonished to hear how his son had lived after being cast into the sea wrapped only in Taranga's topknot. He told his wife their son would be worthy of his name Māui-tikitiki-a-Taranga.

'He has the name of a great warrior and he will be marked out to perform many bold and marvellous feats. He will be one who has no regard for danger.'

Makea prepared the tohi or name blessing ceremony over his son so that he would always be protected. He recited the incantations, but after it was all over he realised he had left out a vital part of the prayers. Makea knew that the gods would punish him and eventually his son would have to die.

## Māui's magic weapon

Māui wanted a magic weapon that he could use to perform great deeds no other man could do. One day while he was staying with his mother he noticed some people carrying baskets of food for an old person. He asked them: 'Who is that food for?' and they replied: 'It is for your ancestress Muri-ranga-whenua.' From that time Māui commanded that the food be brought to him and he would take it to the old woman. But he never gave the food to the half-blind old woman. Each day she would wait at her house for the food, but Māui would throw it away in the bushes. At length the old chieftainess determined she would find out who was trying to starve her to death. By now her stomach was empty and she was waiting to pounce on and eat the cruel person who was denying her food.

She sniffed the air, slowly working around until she came to the west. Then she called out, 'I know from the smell in this breeze that someone is close to me.' She began to feel about with her stick and when Māui murmured something she knew it was one of her descendants. She poked him with her stick and pushed a bony finger into his chest.

'Are you Māui?' she asked, trying to peer at him. After he replied politely that yes, it was he, she asked, 'Why have you been cheating your old ancestress so that I have had nothing to eat for many days?'

Māui stood close to his old ancestress and said, 'I am anxious to have your jawbone. It has magic properties and I want it for an enchanted weapon.'

'Take it,' said the old woman. 'It has been kept for you till now.'

Māui helped the toothless old woman wrench out her own jawbone and then she died. He took the jawbone down to a stream to wash off the bits of flesh and the blood, which flowed into the kōkopu fish. Now Māui had his bright, glistening white, enchanted weapon. It would prove to be his saviour on many occasions.

# Māui tames the sun

For some time Māui had been becoming fed up with the shortness of the days. No sooner had people begun to tend their gardens or gone fishing and hunting than the sun would set and all would be darkness once more.

Māui called his brothers and proposed that they catch the sun with a noose to make him move slowly across the sky. His brothers told him it could never be done — te rā, the sun, would simply burn everything he touched.

But Māui boasted to them: 'Have I not been able to change myself into all the birds of the forest by using enchantments. Now I have the jawbone of my ancestress so my powers are even greater.'

Soon the brothers were persuaded and they set about collecting flax to make tuamaka, or strong square-shaped ropes, and pāharahara or flat ropes. It was from this that the muka or fibres of flax were also twisted into strong round ropes.

When all was ready the brothers journeyed for many days toward the east, the edge of the world where the sun rises. Then they built strong walls to hide behind and set their noose to catch the sun as he appeared into the world of light. Māui told his brothers to keep hidden until the sun's head and shoulders were in the noose.

'Do not let go until I tell you, because I will knock him on the head until he's nearly dead. Don't feel sorry for him when he screams or all will be lost,' he admonished them.

The brothers waited in darkness until the day dawned with the rising of the unsuspecting sun. His fire spread over the land, the mountains and the glittering sea. Soon his head, then his shoulders, were in the noose. The brothers pulled on the ropes and could feel the intense heat on their shoulders and arms as the flaming god struggled and thrashed about.

Now Māui rushed out with his enchanted weapon and thrashed the sun about the head, wounding him badly. The sun screamed out, groaning and shrieking for mercy. But still Māui hit him and only when the poor sun was exhausted and in terrible pain did Māui tell his brothers to let go of the ropes.

From that day to this the sun has moved slowly across the sky, so that the days are longer and the people can go about the tasks they have to perform before the sun dips slowly in the west.

## How Māui fished up Aotearoa

Some time later, when Māui was married and had his own family, he would sit idly at home with this wives and children rather than go out fishing. The days were long and although the family were well fed they grew tired of seeing Māui's brothers coming home with fish while they went without.

They grumbled to him about his laziness in not catching fish, until at last he said to them: 'You need not fear. I have accomplished all things; this is trifling work, going to get fish for you. I will go and get a fish for you and it will be so large that when I bring it to land you will not be able to eat it all. Indeed the sun will turn it putrid before it is all eaten.'

Then Māui made an enchanted fish hook using a sharp piece of the jawbone of his ancestress Muri-ranga-whenua,

with a tuft of dog's hair at one end. When he had finished
he twisted a stout fishing line onto his hook.

Meanwhile his brothers were preparing to launch their
canoe in readiness for their fishing trip. Māui jumped in,
ready to go with his brothers, but they shouted: 'Get out,
we don't want you with us; we are sick of your magical
tricks — you will just get us into trouble.' So Māui was
made to stay home while his brothers paddled off out to
sea to a place where the fishing was good. They were
pleased with their catch and made their way home
determined to return to the same spot the next day.

That night Māui slipped down to the shore, got into his
brothers' waka, hid under the boat's floorboards, and
waited until morning.

The next morning the brothers launched their canoe as
usual and paddled out to sea with Māui still hidden under
the floorboards. When they were well out to sea Māui
showed himself. His brothers were angry and started to
paddle back to shore. But Māui used special enchantments so that the shore appeared to be a long way from
them. When they looked again the shore had disappeared
completely from view.

Māui told his brothers: 'You had better let me go with
you. I can at least be useful to bail out water from the
canoe.'

The brothers reluctantly agreed, and paddled on to their
usual fishing ground. Just as they were about to drop the
anchor and start fishing Māui said: 'Oh no, let's go further
out to sea where the fish are really plentiful. All you have
to do is drop your hook and the fish will follow it from the
depths to the top of the water.'

So the brothers kept paddling. Each time they tried to

stop Māui urged them to carry on. At last they reached the open sea, and sure enough, no sooner had they let down their lines than the boat was filled with fish.

Soon they said: 'Let us return now, brother.' But Māui answered, 'Stay a little while longer. Now it is my turn to throw my hook into the sea.'

'But how are you going to fish when you do not have a hook or a line?' the brothers asked.

They were surprised then to see Māui pull out a magnificent hook from beneath his wrap. The light flashed from the beautiful hook, which was decorated with mother of pearl and tufts of hair from a dog's tail. At its point was a shard from the jawbone of their ancestress Muri-ranga-whenua.

Māui asked his brothers for some of their bait for his hook but they replied: 'No, we'll not give you any of our bait.' Hearing this, Māui doubled his fist and struck his nose violently so that blood gushed out. Then he took up his enchanted hook and smeared it with his own blood before casting it into the sea.

The hook sank down, down until it reached the carved figure in the roof of a carved house resting at the bottom of the sea. But it did not catch there, and moved on past the figure until it caught in the sill of the doorway. Then, feeling something was caught on his hook, Māui began hauling in his line. He strained and pulled with all his might and at last there appeared on the surface the house of Tonga-nui. Up, up, up it came, followed closely by gushing water and foam and then — lo, what looked like an island coming up out of the water.

Māui's brothers shuddered in horror. They opened their mouths and cried out, weeping and wailing: 'Look how he's brought us out into the open sea and now we are surely going to be devoured by this giant fish.'

Meanwhile Māui was repeating an incantation or hiki which makes heavy weights light. He kept doing this in order that his giant fish might come up more easily. In his hiki incantations he called out: 'Where are you Tonga-nui? Why are you holding on so obstinately down there?'

When Māui's incantations were finished there floated up, caught fast on the line, the fish of Māui, a portion of the Earth Mother Papa-tū-ā-nuku, risen from the ocean's depths.

The brothers were aghast — they were stranded, their canoe aground on the back of the giant fish.

Māui told his brothers: 'I am returning to the village to make an offering to the gods from this great haul of fish we have caught. Be courageous and patient; do not eat food until I return and do not cut up our fish but leave it until I have found a priest. He has to make the offerings, prayers and sacrifices and carry out the necessary rites. All of these things must be done in the correct order.

'We shall all then be purified. I will then return and we shall cut up the fish in safety and it will be portioned out to all and we shall return joyfully home.'

But no sooner had Māui left than his thoughtless brothers trampled under their feet the words they had heard him speak. They began to eat food and cut up the fish. Māui had not yet arrived at the sacred place and the gods turned their wrath upon the brothers and caused the fish to toss from side to side and lash his tail about. Mountains and valleys formed where the brothers slashed and raced about the land. If the brothers had not acted so wilfully the huge fish would have lain smooth and flat, a model for the rest of the earth and the present generation of man.

This is recounted as the second evil which took place after the separation of Rangi, the Sky, from Papa-tū-ā-nuku, the Earth. This was the dry land hidden by Rangi and his son Tāwhirimatea. The enchanted fish's head is known as Te Upoko o te Ika, or Head of the Fish, with the fins on either side and the tail in the far north, Muriwhenua.

## How Māui stole fire from Mahuika

Fire was very precious to the world of men, but the time came when there was no longer any fire to be found in the World of Light. Mahuika, the mother of fire, lived in the Lower World; in her children, who lived in her fingers, were the first rays of light which shoot over the sky in the mornings.

Māui resolved to make the perilous journey into the Underworld to ask Mahuika for one of her ten fingers so that he could take fire back to the world. He wandered through the caves of the Underworld, nearer and nearer to Mahuika, his heart full of courage and cunning. When he saw his ancestress he began to tremble and could not speak. Mahuika was both beautiful and terrible to look upon, surrounded in her dark cave by her children, who shone forth out of the darkness.

At last Māui overcame his fear and spoke: 'Oh, old woman, will you give me some of your fire?'

Mahuika cried out: 'Auē, who is this in the light of my children?' Māui answered: 'It is Māui, your grandson.'

Mahuika now asked him the four sacred questions, and

he answered them as he had answered Taranga his mother. When Mahuika knew that it was indeed her grandchild standing before her in the light of the fire she said: 'Yes, my son, I will give you what you have asked for.' And she took one of her fingers and gave it to Māui.

Taking the finger of fire he began his return journey, but when he had travelled part of the way his old cunning overcame him, and he resolved to take all of the fire of Mahuika. He killed the finger Mahuika had given him in a great water and went back to his ancestress to tell her he had lost the finger of fire. And so Mahuika gave him another finger.

He killed the second finger too, and came back once more to ask for another. Māui came back again and again and Mahuika gave him all her fingers until she had only one finger left.

Then Mahuika knew Māui wished to deceive her and kill her, and a frightening anger took hold of her! She took her last child, her last finger, and threw it upon the world and the world filled with fire.

Ah, then Māui began to run!

The flames grew larger and larger and followed him as he ran into the forests and the forests caught fire. He ran to the river but the river began to boil. He took on the form of an eagle and sang incantations for Tāwhirimatea to bring forth clouds of rain. The rain raged throughout the land, bringing with it endless floods upon the Earth.

Mahuika knew she was to die, and filled the world with terrible cries. With great swiftness she ran and ran to save her child, the flame, but the flood and rain always followed her. At last, knowing she must die, she took her last child and hid it in the kaikōmako tree.

Then Mahuika, the mother of fire, perished and died.

And still to this day the kaikōmako tree holds the child of fire so that if the dry wood is rubbed together the flame which once lived in the finger of Mahuika bursts forth to new life again.

## The death of Māui

The feats of Māui are well known — did he not tame Tama-nui-ki-te-rā, the sun, so that the days were longer and men and women were able to cook food, work, play and do things at their leisure; did he not fish up out of the depths of the great ocean Te-Ika-a-Māui, the fish of Māui, Aotearoa; and did he not outwit his ancestress Mahuika, the mother of fire?

One day Māui visited his parents to tell them of his latest plan — he wished to conquer his powerful enemy Hine-nui-te-pō so that the Night might die and man would live forever: āke, āke, āke!

He boasted to his father Makea-tū-tara: 'Ho, old man, have I not done greater deeds than anyone? Who caught the big fish, Te-Ika-a-Māui? Who? Māui! Who captured Tama-nui-ki-te-rā? Who? Māui!

'Truly, old man, Māui will continue on his way for ever and ever! Ha, he will go and kill Hine-nui-te-pō! Hine-nui-te-pō! So that the life of man will be for ever and ever: āke, āke, āke! So I ask you — who is stronger than Māui?'

And his father answered: 'Hine-nui-te-pō, who you see flashing there on the horizon, is stronger than Māui!'

Māui just laughed and said, 'When Hine-nui-te-pō can take my life, then you can tell me how she looks, ha, ha!'

But his father spoke warningly: 'Ah, my son, her eyes which you see flashing are dark as greenstone; her teeth are as sharp as larva rock; the opening between her legs is surrounded with volcanic flint rock; her mouth is like the mouth of a barracouta, and the hair on her head is seaweed. Don't be deceived because her body has human form!'

But Māui only laughed and asked once more: 'Is Hine-nui-te-pō as strong as Tama-nui-ki-te-rā? Is her strength as the strength of the sea which I have conquered and filled with land?'

Then Makea-tū-tara told his son of how when he performed the tohi or name blessing ceremony over him he had missed out a part of the prayers. 'I'm afraid, my son, that is a bad omen. I remembered it too late and it means that you are going to die.'

But Māui turned away, choosing to ignore his father's warning.

Makea-tū-tara looked at his proud, boastful son and realised that his warning had come too late. Sighing, he said: 'Very well, my youngest son. Go bravely there to where you see Hine-nui-te-pō flashing with fire on the horizon and conquer her. Go, my son!'

Māui now took on the shape of a pigeon and flew high up and gathered all the birds of the forest around him. He called to his friends to accompany him on the greatest mission of his life.

They flew toward the west, where they found the old goddess stretched out asleep with her legs apart. Māui told the birds to be very quiet and not to laugh for he was about to undertake his greatest deed: to enter into the womb of Hine-nui-te-pō and to steal her heart so that she might die and man would live for ever and ever — āke, āke, āke! Māui told the birds they were not to make a sound when they saw him crawl into the body of the old chieftainess; only when he emerged out of her mouth triumphant were they to make a noise.

When the birds heard what Māui was about to do they fluttered about excitedly and chirruped, full of fear. They called out: 'Māui, do not do it, do not do it, Māui; no, Māui, no, no; Māui do not do it!'

But Māui only laughed, and after rejecting the form of the kiore, the rat, and the toke, the earthworm, he decided to take the form of the makokōrori, the caterpillar, and began to wriggle toward the sleeping goddess.

The watching birds could not help but be amused at how the great Māui looked while attempting his greatest feat — as a caterpillar! But they all managed to hold back their giggles until, just as Māui reached the goddess' threshold, the little tīwakawaka, the fantail, could contain himself no longer. He burst out into high-pitched, nervous laughter, dancing about with delight, his tail flicking and twitching excitedly.

The shrill sound woke the old goddess and she opened her greenstone eyes and saw Māui. Angrily she snapped her thighs together, crushing Māui with the jagged flint set between her thighs. Alas, it was all over for Māui.

Hine-nui-te-pō always knew what Māui intended to do to her but she also knew that it was best that man should die. And so it was that Hine-nui-te-pō, the daughter and wife of Tāne, kept her promise that all her descendants in the World of Light should follow her down to Rarohēnga where they would return to their mother's womb and where she could mourn and weep for them.

# Tautini-awhitia's journey in the seedpod canoe

# Tautini-awhitia's journey in the seedpod canoe

There was once a man called Porou-anoano, whose wife was Huru-mā-angiangi. The couple lived together happily enough but Porou-anoano was restless and longed to return to his own people.

One day Huru-mā-angiangi told her husband she had a craving for birds, so Porou-anoano went off bird-spearing. Later he returned home with a huia and a white heron. When the woman saw the birds she valued them too highly to eat them and instead kept them both in cages as pets.

Huru-mā-angiangi's craving for birdmeat happened because she was hapū, or pregnant. But before her time came to give birth Porou-anoano returned to his people.

When her son was born Huru-mā-angiangi named him

Tautini-awhitia, and he grew up in the village playing with sailing boats, spinning tops and kites, and catching birds.

But life was difficult for him because the other boys of the village would tease him because he did not have a father like them. One day the taunting became too much for Tautini-awhitia when one of the others said 'It's the darts that the fatherless boy is throwing that fly best.'

He went crying to his mother and asked, 'Mother, mother, where is my father?'

'Your father is not here, he's a long, long way away. You must look towards the sunrise. That's where your father is.'

Then the boy went into the forest, and found a large seedpod from the rewarewa tree. He dragged it to a stream and tested it to see if it would hold his weight and not overturn. Then he went home to his mother and told her, 'Mother, I am going to find my father. I am going to paddle to my father's home.'

He told her, 'I will not stay here a moment longer, I am too ashamed.'

'Wait, son', his mother said. 'I'll cook some food to sustain you on your journey.'

But he replied, 'I'll not eat. A spear can be parried but the thrust of the spoken word cannot be parried.'

Then Tautini-awhitia made ready to go. His mother began to cry, and hugged her son to her as the boy began to push his small seedpod to the water's edge. Tears were smarting in his eyes, too, as he launched his seedpod craft and pointed it towards the east.

Huru-mā-angiangi stood on the beach and in her despair she chanted a karakia to keep her son safe on the ocean. This is her karakia:

Whose is the canoe, whose is the canoe?
It is mine, it belongs to Huru-mā-angiangi, to
Tara-mā-angiangi,
The obstacles in the way are the voices
in the water.
Let the canoe glide swiftly, let the storms
be stayed.
Sail fast, pass through earth, pass through sky,
Go swiftly to the land, swiftly to the shore,
reach your journey's end.
·Let the calm seas be lifted up!

Tautini-awhitia paddled and paddled until he reached his father's home. As he was burying his canoe in the gravel of the beach he was discovered by children from the pā. Tautini-awhitia was taken to the pā and all the children and the adults argued over him, each saying they wanted the young stranger to be their slave.

One little boy, who was the son of Tautini-awhitia's own father, laid claim to him and took him to his father, saying, 'Father, look at my slave!'

Porou-anoano was very pleased and said, 'Take him to live in the cookhouse.'

The next morning the children went off to catch birds, sail boats and do all the things that children love to do. But Tautini-awhitia had more serious things to do and went into the forest to catch a huia and a white heron.

He spoke to the huia, saying, 'This is what you must call: "The fire is not burning, it is dark, dark, dark".'

To the white heron he said, 'You must call: "The fire is not burning, light shines".'

All day he worked with the birds, teaching them to do

his bidding. When night came and the people in the house were sleeping he put the birds in a supplejack cage and took them to the porch of the wharenui. He opened the door and put the cage in amongst the ashes of the fire.

Then the huia called, 'The fire is not burning, it is dark, dark, dark!'

The people all woke and rushed to lift up the cage, amazed at what they heard.

Then the white heron called, 'The fire is not burning, light shines!'

Once again the people cried out in amazement at what they saw and heard.

Then Tautini-awhitia's father stood up. He looked at the birds and said, 'This boy is my son, because these are the birds for which his mother craved when she was hapū with him.'

He clasped his son to him and wept over him. When morning came, he took him to the water and performed the tohi or name-blessing ceremony over him.

---

*Adapted from 'The boy and the seedpod canoe' in* Traditional Māori Stories, *introduced and translated by Margaret Orbell (Reed Books, 1992).*

# Ao-kehu and
# the Taniwha
# Tūtae-poroporo

# Ao-kehu and the Taniwha Tūtae-poroporo

There was once a man of the Ngāti Apa tribe called Tū-ariki and he had a pet taniwha whom he called Tūtae-poroporo. The taniwha had once been a small shark and when Tū-ariki caught him on his line he decided to keep him for a pet. He built a special holding for him at his home in Rangitīkei and performed special karakia on him to turn him into a taniwha.

In time the shark became as big as a whale, and he used to swim from his home in the Tūtae-nui Stream out into the Rangitīkei and back again. Every day Tū-ariki would come to feed him and to perform karakia to turn him into a taniwha. Tūtae-poroporo became very knowledgeable and very big, with sharp spines along his back.

One day a war party came from Whanganui to Rangitīkei. They came upon Tū-ariki, attacked and killed him, then took his body back to Whanganui to cook.

Tūtae-poroporo waited for a long while for his master to return. He had sniffed around in all their usual places but Tū-ariki was nowhere to be found. Then a sign came to him that his master had been killed by another tribe. The taniwha wept for his master and vowed to avenge his death.

He swam down the Rangitīkei River, out into the wide ocean. He sniffed towards the south and there was nothing, and then he sniffed towards the west and the scent of his master came to him. Then he knew that it was the Whanganui people who had killed Tū-ariki.

For a time Tūtae-poroporo made his home at the mouth of the Whanganui River, but there were not enough people to kill there so he ventured upriver. After first trying to make his home near Te Papa-roa Rapids he settled at Purua, where the channel was deep and he could easily attack canoes coming downstream and also set upon those coming upstream.

Confusion reigned along the river. One tribe set out downstream after some of their relatives had failed to return home, convinced that another tribe had attacked them. But when they came to Purua, where Tūtae-poroporo lived, the taniwha rose up before them, causing huge thrashing waves as big as the waves in the ocean. The men behind could only watch in horror as those in front fell into the jaws of the giant taniwha. Then they urged each other to work as one and quickly paddled for their lives to the riverbank.

News about Tūtae-poroporo travelled quickly along the Whanganui River and tribes began to weep and wail, realising that those who had not returned were never coming back. Many left their homes to be out of reach of the rogue Tūtae-poroporo.

The Whanganui River people tried to think of a way they could defeat the taniwha. News came to them that a young man called Ao-kehu, of Puke-rewa Pā at Waitōtara, was renowned for killing taniwha. But Ao-kehu was at that time busy trying to gain favour with Hine-au-moana, a puhi (high-born virgin) of a neighbouring tribe. Even though he had been told he could not marry her as she was already betrothed, Ao-kehu still sought out the young woman and declared his love.

Hine-au-moana replied, 'There are three barriers between us: firstly, I am already betrothed; secondly, my tribe will not consent to our marriage; and thirdly, I do not know you nor do I love you.' To which Ao-kehu replied, 'If there were thirty barriers I would find a way of overcoming them.'

Then Ao-kehu took some small satisfaction when Hine-au-moana commented as she was leaving, 'My people go to war tomorrow. If my betrothed is killed the first barrier is removed.'

The young chief decided to follow the war party, and when he saw that Hine-au-moana's people were in dire trouble he rushed into the fray, turning defeat into victory. Hine's betrothed was found among the dead. That night Hine's people gave Ao-kehu many fine garments and dogs were killed for a feast in honour of his bravery. After the hākari or feast Ao-kehu went to Hine and reminded her that two of the barriers had been removed.

She replied, 'Yes, two have been removed and only one remains. If you can kill Tūtae-poroporo so that our people can live in peace then perhaps I may look upon you with favour.'

So Ao-kehu set out with his men to slay the monster,

armed with his two shark-tooth knives, Tai-timu and Tai-paroa, and with his special karakia. When he arrived at the spot where Tūtae-poroporo lived Ao-kehu told the people to build a man-sized kumete, an oval bowl, with a close-fitting lid.

Ao-kehu told the people: 'After you have set me afloat make your way to the ridges and watch as I am swallowed down into the taniwha's body. But I tell you that once the teeth of Tai-timu and Tai-paroa begin devouring his spines his jawbone will soon be laid out to dry on the shore.'

Hine-au-moana stood on the bank with her people and saw how with one snap of Tūtae-poroporo's jaws Ao-kehu vanished down the taniwha's throat and into his belly. The lovely Hine feared, as everyone watching did, that it would be the last she would ever see of her gallant suitor chief, Ao-kehu.

Once inside the taniwha Ao-kehu used powerful karakia, and called on Tū, the god of war, and on Rangi, the Sky, to help him succeed in putting the monster to sleep. Much of Tūtae-poroporo's strength lay in the spines on his back, and these Ao-kehu weakened with karakia. Next he recited a karakia to bring the monster up to the surface and onto the shore at the mouth of the Purua Stream.

The people rushed down from the ridges, and when the men cut open the stomach of Tūtae-poroporo and broke the lashings of the kumete out stepped the heroic Ao-kehu. Hine-au-moana was relieved to see the saviour of her people alive and agreed at once to be his wife.

The bodies of the men and women found inside the taniwha's belly were taken to the Taumaha-aute Pā for burial and the slain body of Tūtae-poroporo was cut up and left as food for the birds of the air and the fish of the sea.

The Whanganui people were relieved and delighted. Their lovely Hine-au-moana was to marry the gallant Ao-kehu, and at last they could all return to their homes along their beloved river.

# Kōpūwai, the Ogre of the Matau

# Kōpūwai, the Ogre of the Matau

This is the story of Kōpūwai, the Ogre of the Matau, in Te Waipounamu, the South Island. He lived in a cave that faced east, half a mile from the banks of the Matau River. Kōpūwai was fearsome to look at, and was a man-eater. He had the body of a man but was covered with scales like a fish. He had the head and face of a dog, with a nose just like a dog's — long, and with such a keen sense of smell that he could scent things on water as well as he could on land.

He also possessed a pack of five dogs that were as hideous as he was himself. They were swift and fierce, and had two heads on each body. Kōpūwai and his dogs hunted together, often attacking small parties of men and women.

To the south, at the mouth of the river, was a large pā of the Rapuwai people. From this pā men and women ranged

far and wide across the plains in search of food so that the
pātaka, or storerooms, were kept well filled during the
long, cold winter months. In that southern part of Te
Waipounamu the heat was intense in the summer but in
the winter the cold winds blew off the snowy mountain
peaks and kept everyone within the pā stockades.

In time, however, many of their numbers failed to return
after foraging expeditions, and the people became worried
and wished to know the reason for their disappearance.

On one occasion, when a party of men and women were
a long way from the pā on an eeling expedition, a young
woman named Kaiamio became separated from her
companions. She was so engrossed in catching eels she
didn't notice that they had gone on and left her.

As Kaiamio bent down over her line, happily stringing
eels onto the flax twine, she was unaware that the dreadful
monster Kōpūwai and his pack of two-headed dogs were
creeping stealthily towards her. Suddenly she found
herself surrounded by the hideous pack of snarling, rangy
dogs and before she could yell out for help Kōpūwai the
Ogre had grasped her with his massive, scaly arms. Swiftly
he bore her away to his cave, where he set his pack of dogs
on guard in the entranceway so she could not escape.

Until now Kōpūwai had not had a chance to examine his
captive properly, but as he looked at her more closely he
decided young Kaiamio was very pretty and would make a
excellent wife. Instead of devouring her he raped her and
kept her as his slave, to do his cooking and look after his
every need. He devised a plan to keep her close at all times
by plaiting a long flax rope which he then attached to her
hair. As she fetched water or collected wood for the fire he
would jerk on the twine and Kaiamio would give an

answering tug to let him know where she was.

Meanwhile her companions had long since given up any hope of finding her. She had become yet another member of the tribe who had disappeared for no reason.

Many seasons came and went, and still Kaiamio remained in her miserable state of slavery. Life became more and more unendurable as she fretted, longing to regain her liberty and return to her people.

One day she conceived a plan that might just work and give her her freedom. Every day she would go down to the river to bathe and to collect water. Growing on the banks of the river was raupō, a marshy plant that is excellent for building mōkihi or rafts.

Kaiamio collected a little raupō each day, and put it aside until she had enough to begin constructing a mōkihi strong enough to take her weight. She had noticed that when the north-west wind blew Kōpūwai spent most of his time in the cave drowsing. Meanwhile she went about her duties and was careful not to arouse his suspicions by spending too much time at the riverside.

At last the time arrived when the mōkihi was ready. Kaiamio rose at dawn and made her master his breakfast earlier than usual. When he remarked on the early hour she said she had much to do and wanted to get it done before the heat of the day. He appeared satisfied with her reply and fastened the rope to her hair as usual.

Kaiamio was breathless with fear and excitement as she made her way down to the water's edge for what she hoped would be the last time. She quickly untied the rope from her hair then carefully tied it to the springy roots of a raupō plant so that when it was tugged it would rebound a little. Then she pushed her mōkihi out into the steadily flowing waters of the river and held on tightly for the long, long journey towards the safety of her home pā.

Meanwhile Kōpūwai drowsed on. Now and again — as was his habit — he would tug on the line and receive an answer. But before long he realised the answer he got was always the same and the rope remained at the same length. Suddenly he became suspicious. He went outside the cave and called, 'Kaiamio, Kaiamio, Kai whea koe? Kaiamio e?' 'Kaiamio, where are you?' After he had called several times and received no reply, the truth finally dawned on him: Kaiamio had escaped!

In fury he called to his dogs and set off for the river, where he saw Kaiamio's rope tied to a raupō bush. He set his dogs to sniff out her trail but when they returned he realised she had fled by way of the river. He immediately tried to drink the water so that she would be stranded, but as quickly as he drank it the river filled up again. The dogs too tried but the river kept filling up from the lakes at its source.

At length Kōpūwai had to admit to himself that he was beaten, and had been outwitted by a woman. Angry and disgusted he returned to his empty cave to brood over his loss.

Meanwhile Kaiamio was travelling steadily along on the lower half of the river, and at last it brought her safely to her home. As her thoughts turned to her reunion with her family she realised the monster's loathsome scales still clung to her. Quickly she washed herself, then made her way into the pā.

The people were overjoyed to see her, and asked her many questions. The most commonly asked question was, why hadn't she returned sooner? Kaiamio then told them how powerful Kōpūwai was and how when people of the tribe 'disappeared' it was the ogre and his pack of two-headed dogs who were responsible.

When the people heard this they set about planning Kōpūwai's destruction. Kaiamio told them how the monster always slept in the cave when there was a north-westerly wind. They decided to wait until the summer was well advanced, then they made their way slowly upstream. As they progressed they gathered great bundles of raupō and all the inflammable material they could find. Once near the cave they waited for the northwester to blow.

Kaiamio, who was leading the way, approached the cave to see if the monster was asleep inside with his dogs. She returned to say all was well, and stealthily they crept up to the cave and placed the bundles of raupō and other material as close to the entranceway as they dared. Then they quickly set them alight, until the whole was a mass of flames. More and more burning material was pushed into the entrance so that escape that way was impossible. Kaiamio had told the people of another escape route through a hole in the roof, but as Kōpūwai poked his fearful head through they were waiting and battered it to pieces.

Only two of the dogs managed to escape, and they took refuge in a cave. Even today locals can see the stone dogs sitting high up on the ridge with their forepaws hanging out over the mouth of the cave.

# Te Kāpō
# the
# Taniwha

# Te Kāpō
# the
# Taniwha

Te Kāpō began his life as Tū Takapō, and although he was born to a woman he was part man and part taniwha.

His home was at the prow of the Waka of the Gods (Te Waipounamu — the South Island) and he spent his time endeavouring to keep the wild southern oceans from crashing into the waka and sinking it. After one terrible storm he cried angrily to the gods:

'Mighty ones. See these waters that threaten to drown our wonderful waka. Give me the powers you have for one day and I will make Aotearoa ride proudly over the waves once again.'

The gods heard his cry and decided to give him the powers he asked, but they also warned:

'Listen carefully to our words. We will grant your wish and give you the powers you want. But remember it is for one day only and afterwards you are ours and will be part of us.'

Tū Takapō readily agreed, so overjoyed that he failed to understand the full meaning of the words chosen so carefully by the gods.

At sunrise the next day the awesome power of the gods filled him. Mountains moved in his hands; valleys opened at the stamp of his feet; lakes formed where he sat on the ground. The sun still had far to travel and Tū Takapō was so content with his lot that he went to be with the beautiful female gods for a while and enjoy their company. And in his contentment he slept.

When Tū Takapō awoke the day was far advanced and the shadows were lengthening, but he was not worried because he could see keenly in the dark. With huge energy he began to shape the land. He gouged deep channels to form the trails for the Matau, Kaitangata and Waiau rivers.

Once he had finished this he sat back to look at his handsome work, but the first tremors of tiredness moved through his mighty body. So he rested a little. Then, with renewed strength, he carved fjords deep into the western highlands. As he cut beautiful waterways to the sea he used the spoil to build sharp mountain peaks to shed the rain. Then once more he grew weary as the ancient rock drew the strength from him.

The burning stars above showed him his day of power was spinning by. There was no time to rest so he pushed ahead. Shaking with exhaustion he let rocks fall from his hands only to splash into the sea and form islands. All would be everlasting reminders of his tired trail.

Now Tū Takapō began to realise he might not finish his mighty work before sunrise. Regretting the hours he had spent in sweet slumber with the female gods he raced on. He called on all his courage, but it was not enough.

Greater haste led to carelessness. Some fjords were unfinished, several lakes had no outlets to the sea, many riverbeds were too narrow to carry the flood tides, and valleys were closed by walls of stone. Even the tall mountains were affected. The beautiful cloaks of the ancestors, the glistening snows that adorned the mountains, now slipped from their shoulders and avalanched, forming glaciers in the valleys.

By now utterly exhausted, Tū Takapō lay down, drew his legs up and fell into the deepest of sleeps. Where he rested, his body formed Lake Wakatipua and its waters still echo to the beat of his mighty heart.

Tū Takapō stirred as the first rays of the sun touched his body. He looked up at what would be the last light he would see, as the gods came to him and said:

'Tū Takapō, the sharp-eyed one who sees so well in the dark, we heard your plea and gave you the means to honour your promise. But you turned aside from the task and failed.

'Now we come to honour our words. From this moment you are truly ours. We take away the eyes that saw so much. You are now Te Kāpō — the blind one.'

Then, darkness came to shut off the light. His sight was taken and his name. He roamed the south as Te Kāpō — the one condemned to endure the long night of the unseeing.

Now Te Kāpō lives in the deep tunnels he dug. He is still

the guardian taniwha of the south, but his blindness makes it a land of uncertainty — a place beset by snowstorms, avalanches, floods, droughts and earthquakes. When the dangerous days pass and we come to days of calm those close to Te Kāpō know he rests at Ō Māpere, the alpine lake where the wind whistles through the beech forests.

Te Kāpō still labours to clear the waters from his beloved Aotearoa, but as he stumbles through the land he often thinks of what might have been.

# Patupaiarehe — the Fairy People

# Patupaiarehe —
# the Fairy People

The patupaiarehe or tūrehu were a race of supernatural beings or fairies who lived in bush-clad mountains and hilltops. They preferred to live in the dark, misty places where man seldom ventured.

Some fairy tribes were much taller than humans but others were said to be small as pygmies. They were handsome in appearance, with fair skin and reddish hair. Like humans they hunted, made love, enjoyed music — especially the flute — and delighted in holding long talks well into the night. But they were feared by humans because they were known to abduct human lovers — usually women — who were lured away by their hypnotic flutes, the pūtōrino and the kōauau, or nose flute, and they resented intruders and sometimes punished them.

The urukehu Māori of today, who have fair skin and light hair, are regarded as descendants of patupaiarehe through mixed marriages with mortal women. Kōrako or albino Māori, with white skin and pink eyes which glow in the dark, also appear in some families today.

Only three things were able to hold the patupaiarehe at bay: they were considered so tapu that they only ate raw food; they were frightened of fire, and of kōkōwai, the red ochre substance used on tapu objects.

# Te Kanawa encounters the patupaiarehe

On Puke-more mountain in the lower Waikato a chief called Te Kanawa had a mysterious meeting with the patupaiarehe who lived in the misty high peaks of that place.

Te Kanawa had gone with a small party of men and his dogs to hunt kiwi. As darkness fell they decided to sleep the night, and they made themselves comfortable in the hollows of a large pukatea tree, with a big, warming fire built at their feet. Just as Te Kanawa and his men were dropping off to sleep they heard the voices of many people coming towards them through the bush.

The chattering of men, women and children got closer and closer, and Te Kanawa and his men knew the large party could only be patupaiarehe. He and his men were very frightened and shivered into their cloaks, reciting karakia to their gods to make the fairies go away. Only the dogs were undisturbed and continued to sleep on.

Soon all the little people were gazing in awe at the magnificent figure of the handsome Te Kanawa. When a log fell into the fire causing the light from it to blaze up the patupaiarehe would rush away and hide. But once it burned low they crept back again.

Te Kanawa could sense the fairies were getting bolder so he thought of a plan which he hoped would make them go away. He took off his greenstone tiki, the greenstone pendant that hung from one ear, and the shark's tooth that hung from his other ear. These he held out towards the multitude. The patupaiarehe crowded close to look but none would take them from his hand, although they seemed delighted with the items. Te Kanawa stuck a stick in the ground and hung the ornaments on it, hoping they would take his taonga and depart.

But their leader stepped forward and took the shadows of the tiki and the two pendants. These he passed around his people and they seemed very pleased with them. Then suddenly the whole troop disappeared and nothing more was seen of them. The shapes and forms of the tiki and the pendants were taken by the fairies but the taonga themselves were left behind. Te Kanawa had satisfied the hearts of the fairy people by making the offering and showing he was well disposed towards them.

At sunrise Te Kanawa put his ornaments back on and went with his men back down the mountain. He never went hunting on Puke-more again!

## Tāwhaitū is abducted by Whanawhana

Once there was a man called Ruarangi who had a beautiful young wife, Tāwhaitū. They lived in a carved house called 'Uru-tomokia', beside the Waipā River at the foot of the Hākarimata Range. The couple's kūmara plot was at the edge of the forest so that the delicate crop could be sheltered from frosts by tall rimu and rata trees.

One day Tāwhaitū went to the plot to dig kūmara for the evening meal. She gathered the kūmara and put them into a large kit. Then she looked for a flax bush to make a kawe or sling so that she could carry the kit home on her back. Finding no flax nearby she ventured a little way into the bush and gathered tough wharawhara leaves to make shoulder straps.

Now, unknown to Tāwhaitū, a tall, handsome patupaiarehe chief called Whanawhana was watching her from the thick bushes nearby. Silently he crept up behind her, then he grabbed her and dragged her deeper into the bush. Tāwhaitū had no time to scream for help, so suddenly was the abduction carried out. Whanawhana carried her to the summit of a small hill and there he recited an incantation in a high, shrill voice; in a moment the hilltop was enveloped in a thick mist.

Still he carried the young woman higher and higher, until they reached the fortified pā of the patupaiarehe at Hikikiwi, on the summit of Mt Pirongia. There he took her to his home and laid her on a bed of moss. All night the fairy chief made love to the beautiful Tāwhaitū, and in order to keep her under his spell he recited incantations over her and hypnotised her with the sweet, haunting music of his pūtōrino flute.

In the morning Whanawhana sent Tāwhaitū back by incantations to the small hillock clearing he had first taken her to. Much to her relief Tāwhaitū awoke to find her husband Ruarangi anxiously looking down at her. The pair clung to each other, pressed noses and wept. Tāwhaitū told her husband what had happened and said that although she would be safe with him by day, when night came the fairy chief would once again bear her away.

She said his spell was so strong she would not be able to resist him. And sure enough, as evening fell and the mists swept through the village Tāwhaitū vanished right before Ruarangi's gaze. In the morning Tāwhaitū was returned to her husband in the same way, only to tell her husband the same story — that she had once again slept with her fairy lover.

Night after night this happened, until Ruarangi resolved to put a stop to the powerful spell the fairy chief had cast over his wife. He knew that muscle and bravery with a spear or club would be useless against the mana of the fairy chief.

Together the couple sought out the tohunga of the tribe, and he urged them to build a small hut of sapling and fern tree fronds. Across the doorway they were to lay a heavy timber log as a paepaepoto or threshold. Once the shelter was built the tohunga told them to coat the building and threshold with red ochre or kōkōwai, which is made of red earth mixed with shark oil. Only the ridgepole was left unpainted. He also urged them to rub their bodies and clothes with kōkōwai. When all his instructions had been carried out the odour of the oil-mixed ochre hung heavily in the air.

Finally the tohunga told the young woman to prepare an umu oven in front of the house so that the smell of the steamed food would waft around the house and into the forest.

As the sun dipped low Tāwhaitū and Ruarangi clung to each other inside their little hut. Quietly they recited the karakia the tohunga had taught them, while outside the old man kept up his spells to keep the fairy chief away.

Suddenly Whanawhana appeared before the house. His

usual spells to whisk Tāwhaitū away had not worked so he had come to see for himself what had happened. With him were three fellow chiefs from his forest home: Te Rangi-pōuri, Tapu-te-uru and Ripiro-aiti.

Bitterly Whanawhana realised he was powerless to do anything to regain the desirable Tāwhaitū. The smell of kōkōwai and cooked food hung heavily in the air and the priestly chants of the tohunga resounded around him. He dared not go further, yet still he could not bear to give up Tāwhaitū. In desperation he felled a tree, leant it against the ridgepole, and climbed up onto the house, but still there was no way he could enter.

Sadly, he prepared to depart, but before he went he sang this waiata:

> Oh how the north wind presses to the south!
> I sought out Tireni's darling
> And now my heart is full of sorrow
> The banished people are at Pirongia
> Tiki, Nuku-pore, Tapu-te-uru-rā,
> Ripiro-aiti, Te Rangi-pōuri and I Whanawhana
> Are living apart.

When his lament was concluded Whanawhana and his companions vanished, never to be seen again. But it is told that the union between the mortal Tāwhaitū and the fairy chief must have borne fruit, because even today the people who come from the banks of the Waipā have urukehu or copper-coloured hair.

# How Kahukura learnt netmaking from the fairies

There was once a man called Kahukura who was tall and fair. He was known in his tribe as a daydreamer. While other men in the tribe were out hunting and fishing he would sit at home and dream of how he could perform a great feat that would impress his tribe. At this time the fish were caught in ones or twos on hooks and lines, and it took a long time to catch enough for the whole village.

One night Kahukura dreamt of a beautiful white sandy beach with two jagged rocks near the shore. A voice in his dream told him to journey to the far north to a place called Rangiaowhia: 'Come, come north. Come to Rangiaowhia,' the voice told him.

The journey took many days, but early one morning Kahukura came to the exact same beach he had dreamt about. What he saw amazed him! On the beach were the entrails of thousands of mackerel. Close by the little piles he found sticks of flax. Kahukura inspected the area more closely and found only a few footprints on the sand, which did not make sense when so many fish had been caught. Those footprints had also been made at night — not in the light of day.

Kahukura thought to himself, 'This hasn't been done by humans, it's the work of the spirits. If they were men there would be more evidence of them all around.'

That night Kahukura waited in the sandhills by the glowing beach. After a long time he heard the voices of many people out on the water. They were calling joyfully to one another: 'The net here, the net here.' In the moonlight

Kahukura could see them running something out from a canoe, and as he watched another canoe dragged the other end of the line towards the shore. The patupaiarehe sang as they worked:

> Let down the net at Rangiaowhia
> Haul it in at Te Mamaku.

So happy were the fairies in their work that they did not notice the fair-skinned Kahukura step into line to help them haul in the huge catch. When the net neared the shore they called, 'Some of you go out to the sea so that the net does not catch on the rocks Tawatawauia and Teweteweuta.' The names of these rocks mean 'disentangling of mackerel', and Kahukura was amazed that the people did not catch their net upon the sharp rocks.

Before the first light of dawn arrived and all the fish had been landed Kahukura noticed that the patupaiarehe did not immediately divide the fish up as men do, but took lengths of flax and tied the fish they wanted together with a slip knot. 'Hurry, hurry,' the leader called. 'Hurry and finish before the sun comes up.' The sun is the mortal enemy of the patupaiarehe, for if it should touch them, then they die.

Kahukura watched, and pretended to string his fish as the patupaiarehe did. But he used only the short, thick ends of the flax so that his slip knot quickly came undone. He did this so many times that the kindly patupaiarehe began helping him, not aware that the sun was almost upon them.

In this way Kahukura delayed the fairies, and when the dawn arrived they discovered he was a man. They rushed off terrified, leaving behind them their fish and their net. When he took a close look at the canoes Kahukura found they were made from the flower stalks of flax.

When Kahukura returned to his people they were amazed at the magical net he brought with him. No longer would anyone tease him for daydreaming, and he had indeed performed a feat that impressed his tribe.

And so for the first time people learned how to weave nets, from the pattern of the net left by the patupaiarehe. In this way the art of netmaking was discovered on the coast near Rangiaowhia and it was passed on down to the present day. Now many fish can be caught instead of one or two.

# Hinemoa and Tūtānekai

# Hinemoa and Tūtānekai

The great Te Arawa chief of Rotorua, Whakaue-kaipapa, was married to a fine-looking woman called Rangi-uru, and they had three sons called Tawake-he-moa, Ngārara-nui and Tutea-iti. The pair were happy enough together but one day Rangi-uru fell in love with a handsome visiting chief called Tūwharetoa (ancestor of Ngāti Tūwharetoa). Rangi-uru eloped with him to his home on the southern shores of Taupō and from this union she gave birth to an illegitimate son called Tūtānekai.

Later Whakaue won back his wife's affections and she returned to live with him and bore him two more children, Kōpako and their only daughter, Tupa. The family lived on Mokoia Island in Lake Rotorua. Whakaue was a kind father to Tūtānekai, and treated him as an equal to his other children. So it was that Tūtānekai grew to manhood and enjoyed games and friendly rivalry with his three elder brothers. He was a handsome young man and possessed the skill of playing the pūtōrino or flute.

One day the young chiefs were told of the beauty of a young puhi called Hinemoa. Word of her nobility and looks intrigued the sons of Whakaue and they each wanted to have her as a wife. Hinemoa's rank was unquestioned as she was the daughter of Umu-karia, the chief of Ōwhata (ancestor of the Ngāti Umukaira hapū), and of Hine-maru.

At last the young men were to see for themselves the beauty of Hinemoa, as she was to be present at one of the great tribal gatherings at Ōhinemutu. Over the week that followed they each tried hard to impress the young woman, but it was only to the young Tūtānekai that her eyes were drawn. Hinemoa longed to let him know of her feelings but she was afraid he would think her too forward. At last Tūtānekai sent his servant Tiki with a message telling her of his love. She was thrilled and the young couple had a number of snatched meetings together before Tūtānekai and his family had to return to their island home.

One evening not long after their return the elder brothers of Tūtānekai asked: 'Which of us has, by signs or by pressure of the hand, received proof of the love of Hinemoa?' One said: 'It is I who have,' and another said: 'No, it is I.' Eventually Tūtānekai was asked, and he said: 'Not only have I pressed the hand of Hinemoa but she has pressed mine in return.' But his elder brother said, 'No way, do you think she would consider marrying anyone as low-born as you?'

Tūtānekai told Whakaue that not only had he received proof of Hinemoa's love but they had decided on a plan where she would run away and join him. 'I have told my beloved that each night I will play my flute and she should find me by paddling towards the sound of my pūtōrino.' Whakaue looked reflectively at his young stepson and decided he would remember his confession this night.

From this time on Tūtānekai and his servant Tiki would sit on a high balcony overlooking the lake, playing the pūtōrino and the kōauau.

Meanwhile at Ōwhata, on the shores of Lake Rotorua, Hinemoa could hear the lilting, sweet music of her dear Tūtānekai calling to her. But her family had been watching her and, suspecting that she might go to join him, they had pulled all the canoes of the village high up onto the shore.

Hinemoa decided the only way to join her sweetheart was to swim across to Mokoia Island. Taking up six large, dry, empty gourds she lashed them together with flax. Strapping them to her back she went to the rock Iriiri-kapua. From there she went to the pot Wai-rere-wai and, discarding her clothes, plunged into the water. At the stump of a massive sunken tree called Hinewhate she rested a while, then she swam on out into the darkness of the lake. Often she would float on the water supported by the gourds until she had strength to swim on again. All the while Hinemoa was guided by the sounds of the flutes played by Tūtānekai and Tiki.

Eventually Hinemoa arrived at Wai-kimihia, the hot spring on Mokoia that is separated from the lake by a narrow ledge of rocks. Gratefully she sank into the pool to warm herself and cover her nakedness.

Up above her, on the balcony, Tūtānekai called on his servant Tiki to go to a spring near the water's edge to fetch him a drink of water. Hinemoa saw the servant and called to him in a gruff voice: 'Who is that water for?'

'It is for Tūtānekai,' replied Tiki. 'Give it here, then,' said Hinemoa. He handed her the calabash and she drank the water and broke the calabash against the rocks.

'Why did you break the calabash of Tūtānekai?' asked the servant, but Hinemoa did not reply. Tiki returned to Tūtānekai and told him what had happened. Tūtānekai asked, 'Who broke the calabash?' 'The man who's in the bath,' Tiki replied. 'Go back again and fetch me some more water,' admonished Tūtānekai.

Once again Hinemoa demanded of Tiki: 'Who is the water for?' Again the answer came back: 'It is for Tūtānekai.' 'Give it to me,' demanded Hinemoa, and yet again the calabash was dashed to the ground.

When Tūtānekai was told that yet again the calabash had been broken he demanded of his servant: 'Who is this fellow in the bath?' Tiki replied, 'How do I know, he is a stranger.'

Tūtānekai was by now understandably angry. 'Didn't he know the water was for me? How dare he break my calabashes?'

Then Tūtānekai threw on his cloak, grabbed his club and hurried down to the bath. He called out: 'Where's the man who broke my calabashes?'

Hinemoa's heart raced to think that at last she was to meet her beloved, but she was bashful at him finding her naked. She hid under a ledge until Tūtānekai groped along the edges of the pool. At last he caught hold of her hand and cried out: 'Hello, who's this?' And Hinemoa answered: 'It is I, Tūtānekai.' 'But who are you — who's "I"?' Then she spoke louder: 'It is I, Hinemoa.'

Tūtānekai was overwhelmed and as he drew her out from under the rock face she stood before him, resembling a shy kōtuku in the pale moonlight. He whispered endearments to her and then covered her with his cloak and took her back to his whare in the village. That night the two became lovers and, in the tradition of Māoridom, man and wife.

In the morning the people of the village rose early as usual and set about preparing the morning meal. However, Whakaue noticed that Tūtānekai had not stirred from his whare and fearing that he was ill he sent a servant to rouse him. The man went to the side window of the house and peeping in he saw four feet. He raced back to tell Whakaue that Tūtānekai had a sleeping companion, only to be told: 'Go back and see who his companion is.' This time the servant saw that it was Hinemoa, and he shouted out: 'It's Hinemoa, it's Hinemoa in the house of Tūtānekai.'

Whakaue was delighted at the news and when messages were sent to Ōwhata Hinemoa's family saw that she really did love Tūtānekai, and they came in force to Mokoia to celebrate the union of the two hapū.

Today there are many descendants of Hinemoa and Tūtānekai who live around the shores of Lake Rotorua, and many still marvel at their renowned ancestress who overcame all to be with her beloved, Tūtānekai.

# Tūrongo and Māhinārangi

# Tūrongo and Māhinārangi

There was once a handsome young chief called Tāwhao.
His lineage was traced directly back to the *Tainui*
canoe; he was the seventh descendant from Hoturoa, the
commander of the canoe, which had first landed in New
Zealand about the year AD 1350.

Tāwhao was born in Kāwhia to the chief Kākati, and as
he grew to manhood he was betrothed to Pūnuiatekore,
the eldest daughter of chief Whāingaroa of Raglan. The
young couple lived happily together by a lagoon called Te
Whānga, near the entrance to the Whāingaroa Harbour.
Food was plentiful and days were spent on the white,
sandy beach gathering crayfish, paua and kina, and
snaring birds in the nearby forest-covered slopes of Karioi.

The lovely Pūnui was adored by Tāwhao. She was adept
at weaving and other domestic arts and preferred to spend
much of her time at home. Often her family would visit,

bringing with them Pūnui's younger sister Marutehiakina.
She was also beautiful but was more outgoing than Pūnui
and delighted in joining in the poi and posture dances of
the tribe.

Time passed and Tāwhao became troubled that his wife
had not presented him with an heir. Marutehiakina's
beauty, her frolicsome nature, and her beautiful young
body were now often in his thoughts. He decided he would
possess her and make her his second wife.

Tāwhao constructed a tiny mōkihi or raft made of raupō
and on it he fastened his aurei, or greenstone earring. He
consulted a tohunga and learnt from him the ātahu ritual
which ensured that one's message of love would be
returned.

The wind and the current were in the right direction
when he recited his incantations and launched the tiny raft
carrying his aurei across the choppy waters to Horea,
where Marutehiakina lived. The mōkihi attracted the
attention of the young people of the pā and they all rushed
into the surf to try and catch it. Each attempt was
frustrated as the receding waves carried the craft out
beyond their reach. When Marutehiakina joined the
crowd, however, everyone looked on in amazement as the
enchanted raft floated into her hands.

She recognised the greenstone earring at once and in a
flash realised it was a token of love from the blue lagoon at
Te Whānga. The token of love and Tāwhao's message
were reciprocated by Marutehiakina and soon she set off
to Te Whānga. And so, with the consent of her elder sister
and the approval of the tribes, Marutehiakina became
Tāwhao's second wife, or wahine-iti.

Ironically, the two sisters became hapū, or pregnant, at

the same time, but it was Marutehiakina whose son Whatihua (the fruit I gathered) was born first, making him the tuakana (elder brother) to Tūrongo (the renowned and upstanding one).

Tāwhao was delighted to have two sons and as they grew each showed strength of character. Whatihua would often attempt to dominate his teina (younger brother) but Tūrongo would counter by saying that it was he who was the son of the first wife, Pūnuiatekore. So Whatihua and Tūrongo grew to manhood. The elder son was destined for the priesthood and Tūrongo was instructed in the arts and crafts, becoming an expert house-builder, fowler, fisherman and cultivator.

The rivalry between the young men became well-known among the tribe. Often Whatihua's tactics would get the better of his younger brother. One example of this was when they were out gathering kūaka (godwits) on a rocky island in Kāwhia Harbour. Whatihua would use certain incantations just as the birds were gathering around his brother's snares, causing them to fly to his side of the island.

In time Tūrongo could not stand this treatment any longer and he decided to leave Kāwhia and travel south. On his travels he heard of a Taranaki chieftain's beautiful daughter, called Ruapūtahanga, and he decided to seek her out.

The young woman was urukehu, or fair skinned, with light auburn hair. She was idolised by her people and treated as a puhi or high-born maiden. She had her own bathing pool in a small lake, Hītore, and she had a carved house built specially for her and her companions. The house was called Mahuru-nui, 'The Deep Contentment'.

Tūrongo was a tall and handsome young man, but his ardent wooing did not seem to make any impression on Ruapūtahanga. He resolved to follow her when she next went to bathe in Lake Hītore. Silently he watched as she undressed and laid her cloak and garments on low scrub near the water's edge. She waded knee-deep into the water and paused to look at her reflection in the mirrored surface of the lake. It was at this moment that Tūrongo chose to emerge from his hiding place to pick up her garments from the bushes.

Ruapūtahanga heard the noise behind her and turned to face Tūrongo. In an instant she fell face down into the water to hide herself. Tūrongo had a fleeting glimpse of her burning face, which wore a look of surprise and embarrassment. He attempted to shrug off the situation with a little laugh but only succeeded in looking foolish.

Ruapūtahanga decided that this shy, awkward young man should be confronted and made to answer for his actions. She stayed up to her shoulders in the water but looked him directly in the eyes, demanding: 'What is it you are doing to me?'

'It is the love for you that consumes me,' said Tūrongo.

There was silence for a moment, then Ruapūtahanga asked in a more gentle voice: 'What can I do about that?'

'You can do everything!' the young Tainui chief replied. 'I have seen you bathing. I ask you once again to be my wife.'

'It is well,' said Ruapūtahanga after a long pause. 'Return to your home and in time my people will come. Indeed you have seen me in all my nakedness and so I must become your wife!'

Tūrongo replaced Ruapūtahanga's clothes on the shrub

and as he turned away he called back to her, 'I will return to you as soon as you are dressed.'

Later the lovers met again above the sparkling waters of the lake. They stayed together until Ruapūtahanga's companions called for her in the early evening. When they learned the news of the romance between Tūrongo and Ruapūtahanga the whole tribe was stunned, but they were also pleased.

Tūrongo decided to return home before his bride-to-be's arrival so that he might build a suitable house for her. Ruapūtahanga would follow later with a proper escort of her people.

So Tūrongo returned home to Kāwhia and recounted how he had won the hand of the Taranaki chief's beautiful daughter. Whatihua listened and secretly made up his mind that he would win her for himself. He visited his brother's building site as they were about to put the ridgepole in place. After examining the ridgepole he urged his brother to shorten it, saying: 'A big house will take too long to build.' Tūrongo, trusting as he was, took his brother's advice and the house for his bride was made much smaller.

Later, during the planting season, Whatihua persuaded his brother to plant all of his stored kūmara rather than keep them in his pataka for when his guests arrived.

Next Whatihua set about building a much bigger house than that of Tūrongo, calling his house Whare-nui (the big house). He had more workers as his disposal than his brother, and by urging them on his house was completed at the same time as Tūrongo's.

Whatihua had been careful to bring in great stores of kūmara, and he arranged for his people to collect plentiful supplies of pipi, pāua, flounder, shark and huahua (forest birds cooked and preserved in their own fat). Soon there was enough food to feed a multitude from Whatihua's pātaka.

Next Whatihua secretly sent a messenger to Taranaki to tell the people that all was ready at Kāwhia. Proper preparations had been made, and so Ruapūtahanga and her large party of attendants set off on their journey. Her parting from her family was very touching and as they travelled up the Whanganui River they called on many villages and kindred tribes.

Soon the party reached the saddle of a high shoulder of ranges. Ruapūtahanga climbed to the summit of the hill and from there gazed back across the ranges to the snow-capped peak of her beloved mountain Taranaki. The sight of it made her so homesick that she wept where she stood. The hill was thus named Tangi-tū-o-Ruapūtahanga.

Ruapūtahanga and her people were feted in every village they came to, and when they eventually reached Kāwhia their numbers had swelled considerably. Tūrongo was delighted to see his bride-to-be but he had been taken unawares and did not have room to accommodate all his guests, nor did he have enough food to feed them. Whatihua arrived to pay his respects and, just as he had planned, he found his brother in a difficult predicament. He stole a glance at Ruapūtahanga and saw that she was as beautiful as he had heard. Feigning concern, he suggested that Tūrongo conduct Ruapūtahanga and her people to his home, Whare-nui. Tūrongo gladly accepted and soon his bride-to-be was ensconced in Whatihua's home, where her people enjoyed comfortable accommodation and abundant food. Whatihua's hospitality was boundless.

Whatihua next set about pressing his suit for the hand of the young Taranaki chieftainess. While Tūrongo was busy trying to replenish his pātaka with food stocks his wily brother was entertaining Ruapūtahanga with lively talk and witty speeches against his younger brother. When he compared Tūrongo to a 'leaky calabash' the impressionable young Ruapūtahanga did not rebuke him, causing Whatihua to be even more daring in his overtures. His persistence eventually paid off and despite the fact that Whatihua was already married to Apakura, a high-born lady, Ruapūtahanga agreed to be his wahine-iti, or lesser second wife.

Tūrongo was absolutely inconsolable when he found out about his betrothed's change of heart. In his distressed state he completely dismantled the house he had built with such care, dragging the carved pillars down to the beach and throwing them into the sea. His pain was so great that he composed a Song of Sorrow telling of his torment:

> Remain ye, o ye evil house
> Stand o'er yonder
> As object for man's gaze;
> When the centre pillars were erected
> And the walls closed in
> My house did stand forth imposingly
> I built it with knowledge
> Handed down from time immemorial;
> It was the knowledge of Rua-tāhuna*
> That caused (the pāua) embellishments
> To sparkle like wind-blown petals...

Then came the storm;
Moana-nui, Moana-tea;
Manini-kura, Manini-aro**
Alas! now lie scattered along the strand;
Behold! ye all,
All this was to be my legacy;
This was to be the 'Bequest of Tūrongo'
It gave me much joy in the building:
'Twas a woman who gave me the adze of jade***
With which the poles I did so carefully fashion.

Now, O House, I thy parent
Who greatly cherished thee,
Is partaking of the food
From the 'Oven of Sighs'
Restless is my sleep;
Thoughts come and go unspoken,
And many thoughts smoulder within me.
Denied is my desire
To again grasp the adze though gavest me,
And my torrential tears do blind me.
There ye stood, O mine house,
Like unto an abandoned and lonely nest
Within thine courtyard.
Now unclothed am I and naked stand:
Within me lifeless is my soul;
Now, alas! I lay me down and weep.

* A demi-god who founded carving cults.
** Storms at sea of various intensities.
*** This woman is thought to be his mother, who gave
   him the greenstone adze to build the house.

Often the passionate young chief could be seen gazing wildly out to sea and chanting his melancholy song into the teeth of the gale. So sad were the people of the tribe that they too learnt the words and would sing the song in chorus at tribal gatherings. This served to bring Tūrongo out of his depression and he made up his mind to leave Kāwhia for good. He informed his father Tāwhao of his plans and the wise chief then told him that he had decided to divide his tribal domain in two. Whatihua would have the lands from Kāwhia northwards and Tūrongo would settle from Pirongia to the Hauturu ranges.

Tūrongo decided he would travel to the Heretaunga-Kahungunu district, where he had been told there lived a noted beauty named Māhinārangi. But this time he would not let anyone know he was a Tainui chief. Let them see him for himself!

He soon arrived at the village of Kahotea, where Māhinārangi lived with her father, Tuaka, and her mother, Te Rangirangi. Tuaka and his people were busily engaged in building a large tribal house. Tūrongo welcomed the chance to keep busy and he set about helping in the construction of the house. When the tribe went hunting Tūrongo also gained a reputation as a skilled fowler. Before long his skills were being freely discussed and one day Te Rangirangi said to her daughter: 'Me moe koe i a Tūrongo he rangatira mōu: he tangata kaha hoki ki the mahi kai.' 'You should marry Tūrongo and let him be your lord: for he is indeed an industrious food gatherer.'

In the meantime Tūrongo was well aware of the charms of the Kahungunu chieftainess. Māhinārangi was not only beautiful, she was skilled in weaving and she carried herself proudly in the pūkana and the poi. To Tūrongo she

95

was altogether irresistible. In addition to this she was of the best blood in the land.

For her part Māhinārangi had listened to her mother's advice, but how was she to attract Tūrongo's attention? She had noticed that every evening Tūrongo took the same path when leaving the assembly house after talking with the men. One night she dressed herself in her finest woven garments and over her feathered cloak she carefully sprayed the perfume raukawa, made from the leaves of the kawakawa tree.

Under cover of darkness, and just as Tūrongo was strolling home, she ran breathlessly into his arms. He was startled to be accosted in such a way but before he could say anything the young woman whispered in his ear: 'Taku aroha e te tau: taku aroha!' 'My love, O beloved; my love!' Tūrongo was about to say something when she tore herself away and disappeared into the night.

Tūrongo had no idea who his admirer was. Could it be Māhinārangi? He went off to sleep that night with a charged feeling in his chest and the sweet words of love in his brain.

Some evenings later the same thing happened and Tūrongo once again caught a whiff of the raukawa perfume. It was a fragrance he would never forget. He decided he was not going to be caught unawares again. The next day he walked over to where Māhinārangi and her companions were playing the stick game titi-tōrea. Tūrongo feigned an interest in the game and went to stand behind each player in turn.

Māhinārangi had seen Tūrongo approach and she found it increasingly difficult to concentrate as he moved slowly around the circle. For his part Tūrongo could not look at her as he was afraid he would betray himself. If Māhinārangi was not the maiden with the raukawa perfume he would be bitterly disappointed. Occasionally as he leant over the players he could get a trace of the scent, but he could not find its source.

Soon he was almost behind Māhinārangi but by then the game had lost its momentum and her companions had begun chiding her for dropping the sticks when it was her turn. In her agitation Māhinārangi jumped up. As she rose she brushed up against Tūrongo and his whole being quivered as he caught a whiff of the raukawa scent. In an instant she was gone, but one observant young woman later recalled how she was 'almost blinded by the burning ardency of the look' the young couple exchanged.

The rest of the day passed in a blur for the young Tūrongo. Would the ariki, High Chief Tuaka, consent to him, a lowly carpenter, asking for the hand of his beloved daughter. But then, he said to himself, he was also of ariki line — except that no-one in the tribe knew of it. He had purposely not told anyone, wishing only that they like him for himself first.

That night Tūrongo hurried to the place where his love had waited for him before. For a long time he waited — would she never come? Perhaps he was mistaken. Then as the full moon lit up the marae forecourt, a figure came running up to him. In the moonlight he saw that it was indeed Māhinārangi and in wordless ecstasy they clung to each other.

Meanwhile chief Tuaka was in the wharenui discussing plans for the dedication of the newly built tribal house. When the talk had concluded Māhinārangi entered and sat beside her father in the kopa-iti, the left hand side of the building that was reserved for the chief. She nestled against her father and presently looked up into his tattooed face.

'He aha?' 'What is it?' her father softly asked.

Quickly she poured out her love for Tūrongo, the handsome Tainui man. Tuaka smiled down into the flushed face of his beloved daughter and said: 'Ka ora koe i a Tūrongo.' 'Tūrongo will cherish you.'

Tūrongo, meanwhile, was waiting anxiously out on the mahau or porchway. As he came in Tuaka greeted him with a hongi and Tūrongo took his place opposite, at the ihonui or place where the leading chief of the manuhiri, or visitors, sits.

Tuaka saw immediately that Tūrongo would not dare to sit in that place unless he thought he was fit to do so. Accordingly Tuaka greeted Tūrongo as a chief of the Tainui people, then he told his people that his daughter had told him of her love for Tūrongo. Next Tūrongo rose and gave an account of himself, giving the history of the Tainui people and concluding by boldly asking for the hand of Māhinārangi.

Tuaka again rose, and turning to the tribal elders and the company assembled he said: 'I invite you all to speak, for Māhinārangi is a daughter of the tribe. She is as much your child as mine.'

Soon it was evident that the union of Tūrongo and Māhinārangi met with favour from the tribe. Songs and dances followed, then Māhinārangi was conducted from her place beside her father to a place next to Tūrongo that was laid out with the best mats. The tohunga or priest came forward, recited the marriage ritual, and so they were married.

The couple were exceedingly happy living with Māhinārangi's people, and in due course she became hapū, or pregnant. Tūrongo's father was visiting at the time and he asked that his son be allowed to return home so that a fitting home could be made ready. Plans were made for the return, with Māhinārangi to follow soon after as Tūrongo wanted to ensure that his first-born was born on Tainui soil.

Tūrongo, accompanied by a number of his people, set up his home on the Manga-o-rongo, a tributary of the Waipā River. He called his home Rangiātea and it was built so that it had a commanding view of the river plain below. Here he awaited his beloved.

Meanwhile Māhinārangi set out from her home with a large retinue and loaded with gifts. She took with her Tūrongo's dog, which would be useful for catching game and would also be a guide when they reached territory it was familiar with.

The party was feted wherever they went, from the district of Wairoa, to the shores of the beautiful Lake Waikaremoana, and on to Rotorua. By the time they reached Okoroire, just inside the Tainui territory, Māhinārangi realised her condition would not permit her to travel any further.

Preparations were made and beside the hot springs Māhinārangi gave birth to a baby son. The warm bathing pool where she bathed herself and her son was named Te Waitakahanga-a-Māhinārangi — the waters where Māhinārangi bathed.

Soon the party were ready to continue and when they reached the narrows of the Waikato River Tūrongo's dog left them in search of his master. When he saw the dog

Tūrongo wasted no time and with a party set off to meet his beloved wife and his new son. When they arrived back at Rangiātea a huge welcoming party of warriors waited to welcome the Kahungunu chieftainess to her future home.

At the sacred tūāhu, or altar, overlooking Mangaorongo Tāwhao performed the tohi or baptismal rites over his grandson. Tūrongo and Māhinārangi stood arm in arm as Tāwhao lifted up the baby and asked them what his name should be. Tūrongo whispered into his wife's ear: 'It could not be any other name but Raukawa.'

Māhinārangi blushed and with tears of joy in her eyes she looked up at Tūrongo and said simply: 'Raukawa, our Raukawa.'

In the words of the fairy tales of old, the couple lived happily ever after. Indeed, their marriage is spoken of as one of life-long bliss. From this union sprang the great tribe of Ngāti Raukawa.

# Bibliography

Alpers, Antony. *Legends of the South Seas: The world of the Polynesians seen through their myths, legends, poetry and art.* Whitcombe & Tombs, Christchurch, 1970.

—— *Maori Myths and Tribal Legends.* Longman Paul, Auckland, 1964.

Brailsford, Barry. *Song of Waitaha: The Histories of a Nation.* Ngatapuwae Trust, Christchurch, 1994.

Campbell, Alistair. *Maori Legends.* Seven Seas Publishing Pty Ltd, Wellington, 1969.

Ditmer, W. *Te Tohunga.* George Routledge & Sons, Limited, London, 1907.

Grey, Sir George. *Polynesian Mythology and Ancient Traditional History of the New Zealand Race.* Murray, 1855.

Orbell, Margaret. *Maori Myth and Legend.* Canterbury University Press, Christchurch, 1995.

—— *Traditional Maori Stories.* Reed Books, Auckland, 1992.

Pomare, Sir Maui. *Legends of the Maori. Volume II, Maori-Polynesian Historical Traditions, Folk-lore and Stories of*

*Old New Zealand.* Edited by James Cowan. Harry H. Tombs Ltd, Wellington, 1934.

Reed, A.W. *Maori Myth and Legend.* Reed Books, Auckland, 1988.

Te Hurinui, Pei. *King Potatau: An Account of the Life of Potatau Te Wherowhero the First Maori King.* The Polynesian Society, 1959.

——— Anthropology Department papers, Victoria University of Wellington.

Te Maiharoa, Taare. *Folklore and Fairy Tales of the Canterbury Maoris, told to Maud Goodenough Hayter (Mrs T. Moses).* Otago Daily Times, 1957.